Olga Bakes Bread

Written by Joe Hackett
Illustrated by Natalie Hinrichsen

WAYLAND

Olga was very excited as she read her emails. Aunt Rosa would be visiting Nana from America for the Christmas holidays this year!

"I can't wait to meet your sister!" said Olga to her mum, as they packed to go to Nana's village.

"I'm looking forward to it, too. Aunt Rosa went to America to earn more money and I haven't seen her in a long time," said Mum.

8

Soon it was time to get the bus to
the village. When Olga and her mum
arrived, Nana was there to meet them.
It was very cold and snow was falling.

Olga went straight to her friend Mitra's house. She didn't want to go into Nana's gloomy house until Aunt Rosa arrived!

As Mitra and Olga built a snowman,
Mitra told her all about her birthday
present — a brand new computer.

"It's the only one in the village!" said
Mitra, proudly.

Soon Olga's mum was calling her
into the house.

"Olga, can you get some wine from the cellar, please?" called Mum. "It's time for dinner."

Olga trudged inside and began to go down the dark cellar stairs. Just then, her fingers touched something new on the wall. It was a light switch, and it worked!

"Surprise!" laughed Nana. "I had an electric light put down there last month. You don't need to be afraid of the dark any more!"

"Thank you, Nana," shouted Olga.

The next day Olga was helping her mum and Nana get ready for Aunt Rosa's arrival. There was a lot to do. Olga dusted the shelves, Nana cleaned the carpet and Mum made the bed.

"I hope Aunt Rosa brings me a new kind of toy from America tomorrow," said Olga.

Nana and Mum weren't listening. They were too busy thinking about the jobs they still had to do before Rosa arrived.

"We must have freshly baked bread and salt when a special guest comes," Nana said.

"Why do we need bread and salt?" asked Olga.

"It's the way that people in Bulgaria welcome guests," said Nana, proudly. "Come, I'll show you."

Nana showed Olga how to make the bread. She mixed flour, milk and water. Then Nana added an egg and some yeast.

Next, Olga had to push and pull, and chop and punch the dough. It seemed like a lot of work for a boring loaf of bread. At last, Nana popped the bread into the oven.

"I'm going upstairs to rest," said Nana. "Your mum is feeding the chickens so you have to watch the clock. Come and get me in twenty minutes."

But Olga had decided the bread wasn't good enough for Aunt Rosa. Everything in America was much bigger and better!

Olga had an idea and went straight over to Mitra's house.

"Please can I look up a cake recipe on your computer, Mitra?" she asked.

Olga and Mitra found hundreds of recipes and soon she had forgotten all about the time.

Suddenly, Olga remembered the bread
in the oven.

"Oh, no!" she cried as she struggled
back to Nana's house through the snow.

"I'm in big trouble!" she moaned,
when she spotted smoke billowing
out of the kitchen window.

Olga was right. The bread was ruined and Mum was very cross indeed.

"I'm sorry I've spoiled your welcome bread," Olga sobbed.

"Don't cry, Olga," said Nana, giving Olga a big hug. "We've got time to bake again tomorrow."

The next day, Olga and Nana baked some more bread. It looked and smelled delicious.

At last, Aunt Rosa arrived. When everyone was sitting down, Olga offered the bread to Aunt Rosa and Nana passed the salt.

29

Olga told Aunt Rosa all about her cake idea.

"I wanted to make you something even better than bread," said Olga. "I was going to make a cake, just like the ones you have in America."

"That's very kind, Olga," smiled Aunt Rosa, "but I eat lots of cake in America. I much prefer sharing homemade bread and salt with my family in Bulgaria!"

START READING is a series of highly enjoyable books for beginner readers. **The books have been carefully graded to match the Book Bands widely used in schools.** This enables readers to be sure they choose books that match their own reading ability.

Look out for the Band colour on the book in our Start Reading logo.

The Bands are:

Pink Band 1A & 1B

Red Band 2

Yellow Band 3

Blue Band 4

Green Band 5

Orange Band 6

Turquoise Band 7

Purple Band 8

Gold Band 9

START READING books can be read independently or shared with an adult. They promote the enjoyment of reading through satisfying stories, plays and non-fiction narratives, which are supporte.d by fun illustrations and photographs.

Joe Hackett often visits a village in Bulgaria — one of his favourite countries — because the people are friendly and there's a lot of wildlife to see. He hasn't yet spotted a wolf but he knows they are up there in the forests and mountains somewhere!

Natalie Hinrichsen works in her loft studio in a suburb of Cape Town, South Africa. She has been illustrating children's books since 1996 and, in 2005, she won the Vivian Wilkes award for illustration.